SOMEONE'S NICKED MY KNICKERS

SOMEONE'S NICKED MY KNICKERS

Poems To Make Your Toes Curl

by
Gez Walsh

Illustrated by the author

𝕿𝖍𝖊 𝕶𝖎𝖓𝖌'𝖘 𝕰𝖓𝖌𝖑𝖆𝖓𝖉 𝕻𝖗𝖊𝖘𝖘
1999

ISBN 1 872438 38 5

Someone's Nicked My Knickers is typeset by Moose Manuscripts
in Baskerville 14pt and published by
The King's England Press,
21, Commercial Road, Goldthorpe,
Rotherham, South Yorkshire, S63 9BL

Printed and bound in Great Britain by

Woolnough Bookbinding
Irthlingborough
Northamptonshire

Author's note

I'm back!

After reading my first two poetry books, *The Spot On My Bum* and *The Return Of The Spot*, parents and teachers thought it best to keep me and my slightly rude poems away from children. To do this they hatched a cunning plan that had me placed on a deserted island. So, alone and crazy, with nothing to survive on except my wits and Oche Cackie burgers (bought from a burger bar on the island; well they're everywhere now!) I planned my escape and my revenge.

My escape was easy; having saved the tokens off 48,000 Oche Cackie super dooper deluxe burgers I managed to trade them in for a rather fetching red plastic drinking straw. Then I managed to trade this straw on to a passing zillionaire balloonist called Mr Pickle who gave me a lift in his balloon.

As for my revenge, children, I give you...
Someone's Nicked My Knickers

"Cheers mi dears"

I would like to thank the following people for helping to make this book possible:

Steve (I've got to finish editing this history book) Rudd;
Debbie (I wish you'd learn to spell) Nunn and
Phil (you can't count your chickens in this game) Rendell.

I would also like to thank the thousands of people who bought my first two poetry books for having the sense to see that it's about having fun.

This book is dedicated to the memory of Leah, who was a special person and is my guardian angel.

Someone's Nicked My Knickers

Someone's nicked my knickers
And I just want them back.
If I find out who's nicked them
I'll give them such a smack.

I left them in my top drawer
So they would be easy to find.
I can't go out 'till I find them -
Not with a bare behind!

I've looked in my wardrobe
From the bottom to the top,
I've looked behind my radiator
Where I found an old green sock.

Oh, who has nicked my knickers?
Just where could they have gone?
Wait! I've just remembered...
This morning, I put them on!

7

Dirty Gerty

Dirty Gerty
Smells like a pig,
She never has a wash
But doesn't give a fig.

Dirty Gerty
Has bad breath,
Snot around her nose,
Her coat is such a mess.

Dirty Gerty
Smells of wee,
Lays on the floor,
Eats dog food for tea.

I like Dirty Gerty
Though she sleeps like a log.
Her hair falls out on the floor
But then Dirty Gerty is my dog!

My Mother Said This...

"Don't be cruel to animals,"
My mother always said
As she swatted flies with a paper
Then checked that they were dead.

Dyslexia

I suffer from something called Dyslexia
So I find it hard to read and write.
It doesn't mean that I'm stupid,
In fact in some things I'm quite bright.

But I would really like to know,
So teachers please do tell,
Why you gave my problem such a name
Which most people can't spell?

New Age Grannies

The New Age grandmas
Were old age travellers,
Driving an old bus
While listening to the Levellers.

Grandma Moonbeam
Lived in a teepee,
Grandma Sunlight
Just peed tea.

Grandma White Horse
Organised a rave,
Her skirt tucked in her knickers -
Such a scary babe.

They camped at the post office
Waiting for their pensions,
Whistling at old men
Wanting their attentions.

Until the old bus breaks down
The old ladies will be shocking,
Scaring all the old men
By flashing their support stockings.

Dave

There was once a strange lion,
The world it wanted to save.
It was a total vegetarian
And it went by the name of Dave.

Now Dave wanted meetings
With animals far and wide,
But whenever he called
All the animals would hide.

One day he saw a monkey
Sitting high upon a tree
So he shouted to the ape,
"Why are they so scared of me?"

The monkey looked down at Dave
Who looked a big ferocious cat.
He smiled then replied,
"Because you're a lion, you stupid prat."

This really puzzled Dave
As he stared up at the trees.
In a hushed voice he said,
"But I only eat veg and a little cheese."

It was then that Dave saw it,
It was a rabbit off to his right,
Wobbling with an injured leg
And shaking like mad with fright.

Dave could prove that he was harmless,
He knew this was his big chance.
"Let me help you," he roared,
Causing the rabbit to pooh its pants.

Dave said, "Don't be frightened,
Let me clean your wound.
I will lick off all the blood,
You will soon be fully groomed."

But upon tasting rabbit blood
Dave twitched, then he shook.
He apologised to the rabbit
Then quickly gobbled him up.

Dave walked back to the monkey
Saying, "Mmh, that tasted good.
Stuff eating stinky veg,
I'm off to get some blood!"

Now Dave is often found
Eating zebra and the odd gnu.
He no longer wants to save the world
So I'm afraid that's up to you.

The Sniggering Lop Twocks

In our washing machine
Lives a strange beast;
It doesn't hurt people
But on socks it will feast.

Now the name of this beast
Is the Sniggering Lop Twocks.
I have never actually seen it
But it's eaten my socks.

The Sniggering Lop Twocks
Has some very strange quirks
Eating just one of each pair,
The others it shirks.

It lays waiting
Deep inside the drum,
Ready to pounce
When the motor stars to hum.

It selects its prey,
An innocent little sock,
Then eats it with one bite
Like a big bad croc.

So if you ever see me
Wearing two odd socks,
You know it's not my fault
It's that Sniggering Lop Twocks.

Stinky Teachers

Why do teachers
Have bad breath
That to small children
Could cause death
At twenty yards
If I'm not wrong?
A deadly gasp,
A lethal pong.
The reason is
Late at night
Teachers are found,
What a sorry sight,
In your dustbins
Looking for food;
Mouldy old curries
Get them in the mood.
It's all washed down
With maggot soup
Which gives them wind,
It makes them poop.
So if your teacher
Breathes on you
This is what
You must do:
Don't breathe in,
Give them a hint -
Turn the other way
Then offer a mint.

And This...

"It's for your own good,"
My mother always said,
As she slapped my legs
A few more times
Then sent me off to bed.

Frog

There was a little frog
Who looked so very sad.
Someone had called him a toad
So now he's hopping mad.

Ten Strange Presents

A list of ten strange presents
Which I have received from my gran,
Starting with a pocket umbrella
And a plastic frying pan,
A big bingo pencil
With green stripey lead,
A pink fluffy duvet
To cover my bed.
A locket, a bracelet
Some old ballet shoes,
A baby pony poster
And a doll that poohs.
But the strangest present
I have received, by far,
Was a make up kit
Inside a gold jar.
Mum says to be grateful
When gran gives me a toy,
But I've tried to explain to gran
That I'm an *eleven-year-old boy!*

Where's Your Homework?

Smith! Where's your homework?
The dog ate it sir
Oh, ok do it again then

Poulter! Where's your homework?
It just burst into flames, Sir.
Oh, ok do it again then

Rudd! Where's your homework?
It was stolen by aliens, Sir.
Oh, ok do it again then

Rendell! Where's your homework?
Here it is, Sir.
But this is a blank sheet of paper!
It's in invisible ink, Sir.
Oh, ok good lad

Sexton! Where's your homework?
I haven't done it, Sir.
Why haven't you done it?
Because I watched T.V. instead, Sir.
Do you expect me to believe
Such a stupid excuse, boy?

So My Teacher's An Alien?

Our new teacher's
From outer space.
He's not like you or me,
Not part of the human race.

When he's doing sums
He whirrs and clicks,
With eyes in the back of his head
And ears like bricks.

His legs are long,
His arms are short,
If you ask a question
You receive a snort.

But he's not that bad,
I've seen a lot worse,
Like the great white yeti
Who's our school nurse!

Dracula

Late one night,
Asleep in my room,
Through an open window
Flew the prince of doom.

Arriving in the form
Of a Vampire bat,
He changed into Dracula
The blood-sucking gnat.

Pulling back my duvet
He exposed my neck,
His fangs pierced my skin,
Then he was sick.

With horror in his face
He started to recoil,
He'd not sucked my blood
He'd sucked my big green boil!

Granny's Clock

Granny has a strange clock
Which causes much ado,
She's locked a bird inside it
Which keeps shouting out CUCKOO!

My Old Papa

Has any one else noticed
That when dads start to get old
Things start to happen to them,
Like some of them go bald.

Many of them get big and fat
While others lose their teeth,
Most of them gasp for air
As they walk up the street.

They lay on the settee
With a beer, scratching their belly
While shouting at the referee
At the big match on the telly.

Most dads have one of these traits
And I'm just trying to recall
How many of these my father has...
Blinking heck, he's got them all!

The Unicorn

A very strange beast
Is the Unicorn,
Body of a horse
With wings and a horn.

But if we were to find one
This I know would be true,
It would be quickly caught
Then locked away in a zoo.

Strange Story

I heard a story today
About three little pigs
Who had an awful problem
Building their new digs.
The story amazed me,
Though the wolf was a louse,
And I really didn't know
That a pig could build a house.

This As Well...

"Eat up all your dinner,"
My mother always said.
"There are children starving in this world,"
As she threw the ducks some bread.

A Human What?

I must 'ave growed in the garden
Wiv the rest of the greens,
'Cos mi mum has just told mi
That I'm a human bean!

Henry The Cat

Henry the cat
Was lazy and fat,
Never of any use.
All day he would eat,
Lay under my feet,
"I'm tired!" was his excuse.

He'd go out at night,
Come back such a sight
And lay out on the floor.
Then he'd lick his behind,
He really didn't mind
Or care if anyone saw.

But now Henry's past
He's of use at last
And he's no longer so smug.
He wandered too far,
Got squashed by a car
So we made him into a rug!

How Much I Love You

Boxing is my first love,
Football is number two,
Computers are my third love
My fourth is Jiu Jitsu.
Swimming is my fifth love,
My sixth is my pet cat,
Picking my nose is my seventh
And you come after that.

Some People

Some people never listen,
Others never try,
With ears and eyes shut tight
The world just passes them by.

Something Fishy In The Bath

I was in the bath
The other night
When I gave myself
Such a terrible fright.

I felt a fish
Swim past my bum,
I let out a scream
And my body went numb.

But there was no need to worry,
I now feel such a dope
Because it wasn't a fish,
I'd just sat on the soap.

Old Ted

Mum wants me to throw away
My old faithful Ted,
But my life wouldn't be the same
Without his cuddles in bed.

We've been through a lot,
Old Teddy and me,
We've chased away monsters
That only we can see.

The time mum got angry
Sending me to my room,
Teddy stood by me
In my hours of gloom.

And when I was poorly
I gave off a strange smell;
No one would come near me
But Teddy stayed until I was well.

So I couldn't ask him to leave
And vacate my bed;
Besides, I've hidden some money
In the back of his head.

Granny Is A Ninja

Granny is a Ninja,
Deadly at her art.
Try to nick her humbugs
And she will tear you apart.

She goes for her pension
With sword and flip-flop shoes,
Kicks open the post office door
Then somersaults the queues.

She then asks for her money
With sword on full show.
The man asks, "With T.V. stamps?"
With steely eyes granny replies,
"AH SO!"

Victor The Viking

Victor the Viking had a problem
Which weighed heavy on his mind,
It was nothing to do with pillage
For Victor was not that kind.

Victor's problem was this:
His child aged three years old
Was a fussy little kid
Who wouldn't go out in the cold.

Now this wouldn't be a problem
To the likes of me or you
But it was to Victor's son
Because they had an outside loo.

The child would not go out
When he wanted to have a wee
So he'd do it in the kitchen sink
Putting Victor off his tea.

One day Victor was out walking
When a thought popped into his head.
"Why didn't I think of this before?
I'll go home and try it," he said.

Victor then took his hat off
That had horns and was shaped like a mound
Which he turned upside down
And firmly stuck into the ground.

He shouted to his offspring,
"Come on son and park your botty.
Solving this problem has driven me mad
So I think that I'll call it a potty."

Teachers Are Clever

Teachers are clever,
Teachers are bright.
We get sums wrong,
They get them right.

They mark our work
With a cross or tick.
They are so brainy
They make me feel sick.

But they're not as clever
As they'd have us believe,
Because they have the answers
Written on their shirt sleeves.

Ask A Stupid Question

I was doing my morning paper-round
When a stupid man said,
"Where would you be without this job?"
I replied, "Back home in bed!"

Crocodiles

Crocodiles will always greet ya,
Shake your hand then they eat ya.

Summer Walk

It was a nice summer day,
The weather was fine.
I went out for a walk,
Just taking my time.

I walked to the river
Where I sat and stared
At the ducks that were swimming,
The sunlight it glared.

I must have been there
Twenty minutes or so
When I noticed the time
And decided to go.

That is the truth,
Honestly mum.
That's how I got cow muck
All over my bum!

Ouch!

I'm not going to move,
Not until it's gone.
There's a bee on my nose
And it's been there for so long
That my eyes have gone crossed
And there's sweat on my lip;
I know it will sting me
If I was to slip.
People start laughing
As they pass in the street,
Oh, no! Here comes Thomas
With his clumping big feet.
He'll make such a noise
That he'll frighten the bee,
And once it's been scared
It's bound to sting me.
What did you say Thomas?
Why am I standing like this?
Look at my nose.
No! Put down your fist.
Phew, the bee has gone!
Thank you, that was neat.
SMACK! That was for saying
That I had big feet.

Kenny Got Caught

Kenny got caught,
Nicking from a shop.
He got told off
So he promised he would stop.

Kenny got caught,
Nicking from a shop.
They told his mum
So he promised he would stop.

Kenny got caught,
Nicking from a shop.
They 'phoned the police
So he promised he would stop.

Kenny got caught,
Nicking from a shop.
The police took him away
So he promised he would stop.

Kenny's in court
For nicking from a shop.
He has no choice now
Because they locked him up.

Robin Hood

Robin Hood was so good,
Lived in the forest of Sherwood.
His band he called the Merry Men,
Robbing rats the lot of them.
He robbed from the rich, gave to the poor
Until the Sheriff of Nottingham said, "No more!"
But with Robin he didn't want fights.
After all, it's a scary thing, a man in tights.

How About...

"Life is full of choices,"
My mother always said.
"But when Aunt Fanny calls today
You'd better play with Cousin Ed."

Pie

Not far from here
In a field near by
There lives a horse
Who we call Pie.

Now Pie's not like you or me
But he knows more than you think,
He stares as people pass him by
Not knowing what's behind his blinks.

You might think this silly
But Pie knows the morning dew,
He's felt the hunger of winter
And the heat of summer too.

He sees the cars rushing by,
People eager to get home.
He meets the rain falling from the sky
In his field all alone.

Pie owns nothing
But he can feel and see.
He's happy with what he has,
He's not like you or me.

Arthur

Arthur was a great knight
Who didn't know the word fear,
He had a big sword, Excalibur,
And a round table from Ikea.
He lived in a great big castle
Which he called Camelot,
He shared it with an old magician
Who had the catch phrase 'not a lot'.
Things for Arthur were good
With wife Guinevere by his side.
His best mate was called Sir Lancelot
Who turned out to be a snide,
For Lancelot had desires
Directed at Arthur's wife;
When they ran away together
It ruined poor Arthur's life.
They say that Arthur was too trusting
But a friend shouldn't treat you like that.
Merlin could have warned him
Instead of pulling rabbits from a hat.
So Arthur packed his bags
And disappeared to clear his head,
People say he'll come back some day
But after a thousand years he'll be dead!

Cilla The Gorilla

When your head hits the pillow
Do you ever see a gorilla
Who calls herself Cilla
The ice cream seller?
She only sells vanilla
Which she gets from a chiller
Then serves as a pillar
Ten feet high!

Having A Baby?

Mum says that Mrs Thomas
Is a lovely lady.
She has a big fat belly
Because she's having a baby.

I should be happy
But instead I'm sad,
Because by the look of his belly
So is my dad!

Today's Special Is...

Eye of toad,
Wing of bat.
Nose of newt,
Blood of gnat.
Mix them together,
Take a quick look.
This is what's served
By our school cook.

What Cat Eats Ducks?

Deep down under
Lives a duck-hunting cat.
"So what?" you say,
"What's strange about that?
Cats have often eaten ducks,
So what's all the fuss?"
Well in Australia they call it
A Duck Filled Fatty Puss.

The Zip

I had to go to hospital
And I felt such a drip
'Cos this morning I rushed to get dressed
And caught my willy in my zip.

First my body went rigid
Then I let out such a shout;
I gave my willy a tug
But it wouldn't come back out.

So I shouted for my dad,
He started to laugh.
He said, "Let me try."
I replied, "No, you'll cut it in half!"

He then took me to the hospital
Where a nurse asked if I was sick.
I replied, "No, I've just a sore willy,"
Then she pulled my zip down so quick

I shot off that bed
And banged into the door
Screaming, " She's cut my willy off!"
Before fainting to the floor.

So all heed this warning,
It's a very good tip;
Don't rush to get dressed,
And watch out for that zip!

Murder Burger

Something's bothering me,
It's something dad said
Which was "I could murder a burger."
I thought they were already dead.

The School Outing

Yippee! We're all going
On a school outing,
It will be great
When we all start shouting.
I will throw things
Across the school bus,
Getting the driver mad
So he reports all of us.
Then I'll spit pop
Down the back of Clive's neck
And fart in Claire's face
To make her feel sick,
Watch fish-faced Jennings cry
When I start to tease her;
Oh, school outings are such fun
When you're the class teacher!

Fuss About Nothing

I accidentally smashed a vase,
My dad he screamed and bawled.
I don't know why he's so angry
It was over a hundred years old!

They Told Me

They told me
All would be right,
They told me
They would no longer fight.
They told me
They would no longer shout,
They told me
Dad was moving out.
They told me
It was better this way,
They told me
That I would be okay.
They told me
All will be fine,
They told me
That it would just take time.
They told me
Not to cry,
They told me
A LIE!

She Also Said...

"Your brain is very important,"
My mother always said.
Then on seeing my room in a mess
She slapped me around my head.

Who Is My Best Friend?

My best friend in the whole world
Is the best friend that there's ever been.
I don't see him much in the winter,
It's the summer when he's mostly seen.

Sometimes he's very long,
Sometimes he's very small.
He can walk along the pavement
Or up the side of a wall.

He's always very dark,
Never ever white.
He often changes shape
Especially at night.

Who is he?

Answer: my shadow

Vowel Trouble

My teacher asked me today
If I knew what vowels were for.
I said that I'd heard of them
But as for their use I can't be sure.

Teacher said at my age I should know;
The class just gave me sneers.
I don't know why you need them
But grandad's have given him hell for years.

The class then fell silent;
I was asked if grandad was dyslexic.
Not as far as I know,
But his bum sometimes gets hectic.

The class then erupted
With hoots and howls;
Letters that forms sounds
Are vowels not bowels!

Yucky Baby

Mum has just had a baby
Which has left me quite appalled.
How do I explain to my friends
That my brother is bald?
If you think that's not bad
Then there's worse to come,
Because he hasn't a tooth in his head
And green pooh seeps from his bum.

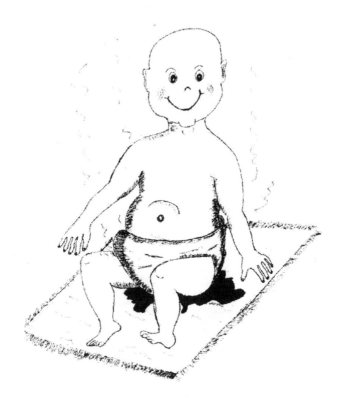

Mad Dog

Our dog turned a bit funny,
In fact it was wrong in the head.
It started eating all the furniture
And it had a wee on my bed.
It would stand so still
As if in a trance,
Then it would savage my trousers
And eat my underpants.
I once tied it in the yard
Calling it a prat,
When I called back later
He'd eaten next door's cat!
"I'm going to get rid,"
My mum explained
As it rubbed itself on her leg
While barking quite insane.
So that was it,
We got rid the next morning;
He went to a dog's home,
We didn't give any warnings.
But as time passed
We forgot our strange pet,
That was until the news flash -
Mad dog eats vet!

Early Birds

Early birds catch the worms
People often say,
But I wonder what would happen
If the worms didn't come out to play?

The birds would all start waiting
Forming massive queues,
Some would start pushing in
Saying, "I'm before you."

Then there would be arguments
Leading to a fight,
Rioting would then follow
Until late into the night.

The police would have to be called,
Birds would be dragged away,
And all of this because
The worms wouldn't come out to play.

You must stop this from happening,
In your garden take care.
Concrete it all over
And tell the birds to go elsewhere.

The Worst Thing That Can Happen To Wellies

The worst thing that can happen to wellies,
That's what happened to me today.
What's the worst thing that can happen to wellies
I hear you all say?
Well when you're wading out in water
And you forget to stop,
The water starts to rise up your wellies
And ends up spilling over the top.
It fills up your boots
So you start jumping and reeling,
This my friends is what we call
The worst thing that can happen to wellies' feelings.

Hiccup!

I can't stop hic...
I can't stop hic...
I can't stop hic...
HICCUP!
Hic I...
Hic I...

The Parachute Jump

Grandad once told me
That during the war
He jumped from an aeroplane
And started to soar.

But on pulling his ripcord
He screamed, "That's done it!"
As it came off in his hand
And to the ground he did plummet.

As he fell to earth
With fear in his eyes
A man passed him going up,
Much to his surprise.

The man's clothes were burnt
And his face was all black,
He shot up past grandad
Nearly giving him a heart attack.

But grandad screamed to the man
With howls and hoots
"Excuse me young man,
Do you know any thing about parachutes?"

The man replied, "No!"
As he sped to the heavens,
Then he shouted to grandad
"Do you know anything about gas ovens?"

If

If grass**hop**pers hop,
Humming birds hum,
Flying fish fly,
Do **bum**ble bees bum?

The Rock And Roll Band

I want to play
In a rock and roll band,
Out with super-models
Walking hand in hand.
I want lots of girls
Screaming for me,
Eat in fancy restaurants
All for free.
This is what I want
But I can't sing or play,
But then neither can most boy bands
And they all seem to do okay.

Sis Loves An Alien

My sister arrived home
Late last night
With her new boyfriend
Who gave us all a fright.

He was about six foot four
With bright green hair,
The spots on his face
Gave the dog an awful scare.

I think he's an alien,
He has a strange walk.
Even my dad asked,
"Can it talk?"

Sis says that we're horrid
And she thinks that he's cute.
I think he's from Mars
And his space ship's his boots.

I Love Jane Tully

I love Jane Tully
But she doesn't love me,
I'm so broken-hearted
Though no one takes it seriously.

I was her boyfriend
For quite some time;
Now she's going out with Craig
So she's no friend of mine.

Sometimes I see them together,
This makes me feel sad.
I once saw them kissing;
That hurt like mad.

Mum says I'll get over it,
That I'm silly and young.
But it hurts me so much,
Why can't you see this, mum?

Stop Sulking!

Alan always starts sulking
If he can't get his own way.
Ugh! Eh! What!
Is all that he will say?

He always tells you you're wrong,
Even if you're right.
You can't stop him sulking,
Try as you might.

So to people like Alan
Don't give a second look.
Tell them to get a life
And for heaven's sake GROW UP!

Three Blind Mice

Three blind mice,
See how they run,
It made them sweat
The farmer's wife's threat
Of a carving knife up the bum!

Big Bad Witch

There is a big bad witch
Who lives down our street,
But she can't catch children
Because she's got bad feet.

Her broomstick's broken,
She's feeling rather sad,
She would love to cook a child
But her corns hurt like mad.

The kids knock on her door,
Then they run away.
She would make them into a stew
If she had her way.

So until her corns are fixed
She can't chase them down the road.
No more eating small children,
She'll have to keep on eating toads.

Then She Said...

"Alcohol is bad for you,"
My mother always said.
Then she went out on Friday night
To paint the town red.

Poor Little Fly

We were out driving one summer
When a poor little fly
Splatted against our windscreen,
What an awful way to die!

What last went through its head
When it died in the midday sun?
I know the last thing through its head
Was definitely its bum!

Sing A Song Of Sixpence

Sing a song of sixpence
I like fried rice,
Four to twenty four
Really are quite nice.
When the take-away opens
The people all rush in,
A chop suey dish is what I wish
And make my prawns king.

Sea How I Write

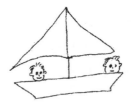

My teacher says that my handwriting
Reminds her of the sea.
I wonder why this could be?

Big Harold Webster

Big bad Harold Webster
He's going to beat me up.
I wish some one would save me
From this big bad crook.
He demanded my dinner money
But I said no!
So he twisted my arm
But the Head made him let go.
He's spooked me all day
By pointing to the clock,
Punching his fist with menace
Then starting to mock.
I know I should ignore him,
Just keep out of his way;
But I'm his class teacher
So I'm with him all day.

Praying To Win

The coach of our football team
Is the local vicar.
He hopes to win just one game
So he prays that we'll run quicker.

Down In One

After eating his dinner
The snake he croaked.
He said, "I'm ever so sorry,
But I've a frog in my throat."

How To Use A Hedgehog

If you were to frighten a hedgehog
It would roll itself into a ball,
So people say that they're of no use,
Of no use at all.

But they do have their uses
And many gardeners they please,
Because if you tie them to a long stick
You can use them to pick up leaves.

Driving Dad Mad

No one can drive
Quite as good as dad,
'Cos when we're out in the car
He swears like mad
At all the other drivers
Out on the road -
He once cursed a vicar
Calling him a warty toad.
"Women are the worst,"
Dad will always say.
"Just what is she doing?
Come on, woman, I haven't all day!"
He blasts his horn
When cars come to a halt;
He's had a few crashes
But they weren't his fault.
Yes, the highways are dangerous,
All road users are mad.
There's only one safe driver,
And that's my dad.

Pa Popped In

It was early one evening,
We were all watching telly,
Mum was picking her nose
While scratching her belly.

My sister and me
Were sat on the settee,
The dog was sprawled out
In front of the T.V.

When as if from nowhere
Came a terrible smell,
We all covered our noses -
We didn't feel well.

On looking around
For someone to blame
No one had noticed
Pa had popped in, pooped
And popped out again.

Mum blamed the dog
Saying, "Dirty beast!"
Sis blamed me
For eating too much cheese.

I pointed in the direction
From where the smell had come;
With an accusing finger
I said, "It was mum!"

The dog growled at my sister
"Don't sit there so smart."
I think he blamed her
For that humungous fart.

But still no one knew
Who was really to blame,
That pa had popped in, pooped
And popped out again.

As the smell was going
We could now breathe free;
Mum read a magazine,
We watched T.V.

The dog fell back to sleep,
He was so relaxed,
Not one of us knew
Who was grinning at our backs

Because the smell returned
Like a dirty drain,
Pa had popped in, pooped
And popped out again.

We grasped our throats,
All very irate;
The dog shook his head
Saying, "It wasn't me mate!"

Well if it's not us,
Who could it be?
When in walked pa saying,
"That smell belongs to me."

So the problem's been solved,
It was driving us insane;
Pa has now promised
Not to pop in,
Poop and pop out again.

The Stogey Bogey

(This poem should be sung to the tune of the
Hokey Cokey.)

First take your finger,
Stick it up your snout
Then pick a stogey bogey
And pull it back out.

Check if it's like rubber,
All green and thin,
Or is it a corn flake
With black bits in?

Oh, roll that stogey bogey!
Oh, roll that stogey bogey!
Use your finger and thumb
Until it feels like gum
Then you flick it all about.

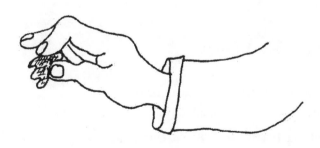

Why We Need Trees

Out in darkest Africa
There lives a poor dog
Who walks with crossed legs
Because it needs the bog.
But there's a problem
Before it can pee,
It needs to find
A nice shady tree.
But with drought and famine
Most trees have gone,
Leaving the dog's willy swollen
And its bladder like a time-bomb.
So I hope people soon realise
And all plant just one tree,
If not for the people of Africa,
Please - let the dog have a pee!

Dud Rubber

I once bought a rubber plant
With my weekly allowance,
Then I threw it against the wall
But the stupid thing didn't bounce.

Sweeney Todd

If you go to my hairdresser's
You'll have to be quite brave,
'Cos Sweeney Todd's my barber
So you get a real close shave.
You may not have heard of him,
But I tell no lies;
Always visit him in twos
And don't eat any of his pies.

My Future Career

What should I do
When I leave school?
I'm not working hard
Because I'm nobody's fool.

No long hours,
Not night and day.
Lots of time off
With lots of pay.

No stupid uniform
That's totally uncool,
It's bad enough
Wearing one for school.

I know, I've got it!
A job with cheer -
I'll replace Santa
And work one night a year.

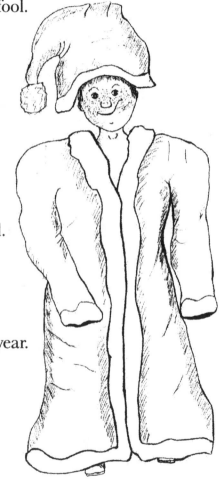

The Swap

Could someone please help?
I think I need some advice,
'Cos I've done a swap with Damion -
He's taken four of my pet mice.
At first I thought it a good swap,
But I now think it a mistake,
And mum's going to go mental
When she sees my new eight foot snake.

What's That?

Once two little turds
Were having a chat
When something fell on them
With one heck of a splat.
One said, "That's horrid!"
The other said, "Stand clear!
"Move somewhere else,
It's dire 'ere."

Why should I?

I have to do the washing up
Which is something I really hate.
And why should I wash all the dishes
When I only used one plate?

Holiday Pain

This year we're off to sunny Spain,
Last year mum said she wouldn't go there again
Because my dad got drunk in a bar
Then in the swimming pool he undid mum's bra.
She screamed as her busters nearly fell out
So she gave my dad such a clout.
She said it had ruined her holiday
And, boy, did she make dad pay.
He had a very quiet week
Because to him my mum wouldn't speak.
But they've decided to give it another go,
And dad has promised his drinking shall be slow.
But I know it will all happen again;
That's clear, because he does the same
Every flipping year!

Frog Head

The doctor was in his surgery
Trying to invent a cure,
When all of a sudden
There was a knock at the door.
The doctor shouted, "Enter!
Come lay upon the bed,"
When in walked a small boy
With a frog stuck to his head.
The doctor pulled at the frog
Then he had a close look;
It was growing from his head
So he looked in a book.
The doctor said, "It's amazing.
"How did this start, son?"
The frog then replied,
"As a spot on my bum."

A Young Man From Crewe

There was a young man from Crewe,
Who was dying to use the loo.
But he received on his back
A mighty big smack
And filled his pants with pooh.

Finally...

"Family life's important,"
My mother always said,
Looking at dad asleep in his chair
And wishing she wasn't wed.

Crying For Help

She hears the screaming
From the next bedroom.
With tear-filled eyes
She peers through the gloom,

Footsteps stamping
To her bedroom door.
She holds her breath,
Can't take no more.

The door slams open,
He strides in,
She begs for mercy
But there's none from him.

Cowering with fear
On her filth-ridden bed
He smashes his fist
Into her small frail head.

Her body falls limp,
Blood trickles from her mouth.
"You deserved it," he sneers,
Then the brute walks out.

Her life ebbs away,
Why did it get to this state?
There are people who help,
But for her I'm afraid it's too late.